CW00556553

Wildlife **Photographer** of the Year
Diary 2012

Published by the Natural History Museum, London

The pictures gathered in this diary are prize-winning or commended images from past years of the Wildlife Photographer of the Year competition – the international showcase for the very best photography featuring natural subjects. It is owned by two UK institutions that pride themselves on revealing and championing the diversity of life on Earth: the Natural History Museum and *BBC Wildlife Magazine*.

The origins of the competition go back to 1964, when *BBC Wildlife Magazine* was called *Animals* and there were just three categories and about 600 entries. It grew in stature over the years and, in 1984, *BBC Wildlife Magazine* and the Natural History Museum joined forces to create the competition as it is today.

Open to visitors since 1881, the Natural History Museum looks after a world-class collection of 70 million specimens. It is also a leading scientific-research institution, with ground-breaking projects in more than 68 countries. About 300 scientists work at the Museum, researching the valuable collections to better understand life on Earth. Every year more than three million visitors, of all ages and levels of interest, are welcomed through the Museum's doors.

Wildlife Photographer of the Year is one of the most popular of the Museum's exhibitions. Visitors come not only to see breathtaking imagery, but also to understand some of the threats faced by our planet's animals and plants. Understanding and finding ways of conserving the Earth's biodiversity is at the heart of the Museum's work. This exhibition is one way to share that mission with others, encouraging us to see the environment around us with new eyes.

For more than 40 years *BBC Wildlife Magazine* has celebrated and shared the miracle and beauty of nature with its readers.

Every issue is packed with inspirational images by the world's best photographers – many of them Wildlife Photographer of the Year award-winners and informative, entertaining features by experts.

We reveal how to get closer to Britain's magnificent wildlife, enjoy great days out and attract everything from bugs to badgers to your garden. Plus, stay up to date with the latest conservation issues, environmental news and scientific discoveries from around the globe.

To find out more about *BBC Wildlife Magazine*, improve your own wildlife photography and enter our readers' competition, visit www.bbcwildlifemagazine.com

JANUARY

M	T	W	Th	F	S	S
						1
2	3	4	5	6	7	8
9	10	11	12	13	14	15
16	17	18	19	20	21	22
23	24	25	26	27	28	29
30	31					

FEBRUARY

wk	M	T	W	Th	F	S	S
6			1	2	3	4	5
7	6	7	8	9	10	11	12
8	13	14	15	16	17	18	19
9	20	21	22	23	24	25	26
10	27	28	29				

MARCH

wk	M	T	W	Th	F	S	S
10				1	2	3	4
11	5	6	7	8	9	10	11
12	12	13	14	15	16	17	18
13	19	20	21	22	23	24	25
14	26	27	28	29	30	31	

APRIL

wk	M	T	W	Th	F	S	S
14							1
15	2	3	4	5	6	7	8
16	9	10	11	12	13	14	15
17	16	17	18	19	20	21	22
18	23	24	25	26	27	28	29
19	30						

MAY

M	T	W	Th	F	S	S
	1	2	3	4	5	6
7	8	9	10	11	12	13
14	15	16	17	18	19	20
21	22	23	24	25	26	27
28	29	30	31			

JUNE

wk	M	T	W	Th	F	S	S
23					1	2	3
24	4	5	6	7	8	9	10
25	11	12	13	14	15	16	17
26	18	19	20	21	22	23	24
27	25	26	27	28	29	30	

JULY

wk	M	T	W	Th	F	S	S
27							1
28	2	3	4	5	6	7	8
29	9	10	11	12	13	14	15
30	16	17	18	19	20	21	22
31	23	24	25	26	27	28	29
32	30	31					

AUGUST

wk	M	T	W	Th	F	S	S
32			1	2	3	4	5
33	6	7	8	9	10	11	12
34	13	14	15	16	17	18	19
35	20	21	22	23	24	25	26
36	27	28	29	30	31		

SEPTEMBER

M	T	W	Th	F	S	S
					1	2
3	4	5	6	7	8	9
10	11	12	13	14	15	16
17	18	19	20	21	22	23
24	25	26	27	28	29	30

OCTOBER

wk	M	T	W	Th	F	S	S
41	1	2	3	4	5	6	7
42	8	9	10	11	12	13	14
43	15	16	17	18	19	20	21
44	22	23	24	25	26	27	28
45	29	30	31				

NOVEMBER

wk	M	T	W	Th	F	S	S
45				1	2	3	4
46	5	6	7	8	9	10	11
47	12	13	14	15	16	17	18
48	19	20	21	22	23	24	25
49	26	27	28	29	30		

DECEMBER

wk	M	T	W	Th	F	S	S
49						1	2
50	3	4	5	6	7	8	9
51	10	11	12	13	14	15	16
52	17	18	19	20	21	22	23
53	24	25	26	27	28	29	30
1	31						

JANUARY

M	T	W	Th	F	S	S
1	2	3	4	5	6	
7	8	9	10	11	12	13
14	15	16	17	18	19	20
21	22	23	24	25	26	27
28	29	30	31			

FEBRUARY

wk	M	T	W	Th	F	S	S
5					1	2	3
6	4	5	6	7	8	9	10
7	11	12	13	14	15	16	17
8	18	19	20	21	22	23	24
9	25	26	27	28			

MARCH

wk	M	T	W	Th	F	S	S
9					1	2	3
10	4	5	6	7	8	9	10
11	11	12	13	14	15	16	17
12	18	19	20	21	22	23	24
13	25	26	27	28	29	30	31

APRIL

wk	M	T	W	Th	F	S	S
14	1	2	3	4	5	6	7
15	8	9	10	11	12	13	14
16	15	16	17	18	19	20	21
17	22	23	24	25	26	27	28
18	29	30					

MAY

M	T	W	Th	F	S	S
	1	2	3	4	5	
6	7	8	9	10	11	12
13	14	15	16	17	18	19
20	21	22	23	24	25	26
27	28	29	30	31		

JUNE

wk	M	T	W	Th	F	S	S
22						1	2
23	3	4	5	6	7	8	9
24	10	11	12	13	14	15	16
25	17	18	19	20	21	22	23
26	24	25	26	27	28	29	30

JULY

wk	M	T	W	Th	F	S	S
27	1	2	3	4	5	6	7
28	8	9	10	11	12	13	14
29	15	16	17	18	19	20	21
30	22	23	24	25	26	27	28
31	29	30	31				

AUGUST

wk	M	T	W	Th	F	S	S
31				1	2	3	4
32	5	6	7	8	9	10	11
33	12	13	14	15	16	17	18
34	19	20	21	22	23	24	25
35	26	27	28	29	30	31	

SEPTEMBER

M	T	W	Th	F	S	S
						1
2	3	4	5	6	7	8
9	10	11	12	13	14	15
16	17	18	19	20	21	22
23	24	25	26	27	28	29
30						

OCTOBER

wk	M	T	W	Th	F	S	S
40		1	2	3	4	5	6
41	7	8	9	10	11	12	13
42	14	15	16	17	18	19	20
43	21	22	23	24	25	26	27
44	28	29	30	31			

NOVEMBER

wk	M	T	W	Th	F	S	S
44					1	2	3
45	4	5	6	7	8	9	10
46	11	12	13	14	15	16	17
47	18	19	20	21	22	23	24
48	25	26	27	28	29	30	

DECEMBER

wk	M	T	W	Th	F	S	S
48							1
49	2	3	4	5	6	7	8
50	9	10	11	12	13	14	15
51	16	17	18	19	20	21	22
52	23	24	25	26	27	28	29
53	30	31					

26 *Monday*

27 *Tuesday*

28 *Wednesday*

9	Thursday			

0	Friday	*Carmina Burana 7.30 B'ham*		

1	Saturday	New Year's Eve Hogmanay (Scotland)	**1**	Sunday	New Year's Day

Snowy landing
by Vincent Munier

A snowy owl comes in to land in north Quebec, Canada, where Vincent fulfilled his dream of spending time with them. 'I've usually had to photograph European birds from hides,' says Vincent, 'so it was a surprise to find the owls were unperturbed by my presence and I could move freely in the open.' This year-old youngster became a favourite. 'Sitting in the snow from dawn till dusk, I got to know its character.' The soft grey-blue sky provided the ideal backdrop to show off its 'sheer perfection'.

Nikon D200 with 300mm f2.8 AFS lens; 1/4000 sec at f4.5; 200 ISO; tripod.v.

....

2 *Monday*   Holiday (UK, Rep. Ireland, Australia, Canada, USA

....

3 *Tuesday*   Holiday (Scotland

....

4 *Wednesday*

Ice hole
by Baard Næss
Baard was searching for polar bears on Svalbard,
an Arctic island north of Norway, but bitter winds,
snowstorms and heavy clouds made the going
tough. 'When we got off the snow-scooters for a
rest,' says Baard, 'I spotted a seal breathing hole
and saw stirrings. I waited motionlessly right next
to it – a bit like a polar bear might do – until a
head popped up.' In the event, the grey light was
perfect. Any harsher and the subtle colours would
have been lost and the contrast between the
ringed seal and its icy environment too great.

*Canon 1D Mark II with 70–200mm f2.8L lens;
1/200 sec at f5.6; 400 ISO.*

Thursday

Friday   Epiphany (Christian)

Saturday   **8**   Sunday

9   *Monday*   *Full moon*

10 *Tuesday*

11 *Wednesday*

Skeleton Coast
by Andy Biggs
'As I peered through the scratched airplane window, I wondered how I could convey the giddy heights of the Namibian sand-dunes. I wanted to capture the way shafts of sun pierce the mist and highlight the sand textures. The huddle of Cape fur seals – a dark smudge on the strip of beach – gave a sense of the vastness of this wilderness.' The Skeleton Coast is 16,000 square kilometres of national park that runs along the Atlantic coast of Namibia. The plants and animals that live there get their moisture from the dense ocean fogs, which form as the cold Benguela current blows inland.

Canon EOS 5D + 24–105mm lens at 47mm; 1/1250 sec at f5.6; ISO 500.

16 Monday

17 Tuesday

18 Wednesday

Big baby nap
by Claudio Contreras Koob
'I was photographing wildlife on Guadalupe
Island off the coast of Mexico as part of a major
scientific project, and watched this elephant seal
weanling splash around in the surf and then haul
up onto the beach and fall asleep. It's a dangerous
time, as big, plump babies with limited swimming
skills attract great white sharks.' Female elephant
seals go without food while they nurse their
pups. By the time the pup is weaned, its mother is
starving and abandons it to go in search of food –
the youngsters are left to fend for themselves.

*Canon EOS-1Ds Mark II + Canon 300mm f2.8 IS
USM lens + 2x II extender EF; 1/60 sec at f10; ISO
200; Gitzo tripod.*

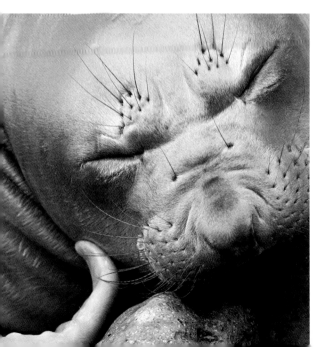

23 *Monday*

New moon ●
Chinese New Year (Year of the Dragon

24 *Tuesday*

25 *Wednesday*

Burns Night (Scotland

Flight of the albatross
by Pat Douglass
Friend to the sailor and icon of the long-distance
traveller, an albatross can soar for thousands of
kilometres without touching land. South of the
Falkland Islands off the tip of South America, on a
ship heading for South Georgia, Pat was 'trying to
photograph birds as they skimmed along the water,
rising and falling on the air currents at the stern.'
As this black-browed albatross dipped close to
the water, its wave-rippled reflection provided the
extra dimension she was after. 'I knew I had caught
an image symbolic of my journey in the Southern
Ocean.' It is also an image few may be able to
photograph in the future. So many albatrosses
have died on the hooks of longline fisheries that
the species is now highly endangered.

*Canon 5D with 300mm f4 lens and 1.4x converter;
1/640 sec at f8; 200 ISO.*

26	Thursday	Australia Day, Holiday (Australia)
27	Friday	Holocaust Memorial Day
28	Saturday	**29** Sunday

....

30 *Monday*

....

31 *Tuesday*

....

1 *Wednesday*

Swallowtail salt-sipping
by Bill Harbin
'Looking through binoculars beside a stream in
Mexico, I was struck by the power of the head-
on image – large black eyes, contrasting yellow
face and long proboscis. By crawling on my
stomach through the mud and sand to within
30 centimetres of the butterfly, I managed to
capture the dramatic perspective I wanted.' The
giant swallowtail butterfly uses its proboscis, a
straw-like feeding tube, to suck up nectar from
plants but it cannot get all the nutrients it needs
to survive from nectar alone. Because of this, it
feeds from puddles of mud or wet sand to get
the missing yet valuable salts and minerals, this
is called puddling.

*Canon EOS-1D Mark III + 180mm macro lens +
1.4x teleconverter; 1/125 sec at f9; ISO 400;
Canon 580EX flash + ETTL2.*

Thursday

Friday

Saturday   *Milad un Nabi.*   **5**   Sunday
            Birthday of the Prophet
            Muhammad (Islamic)

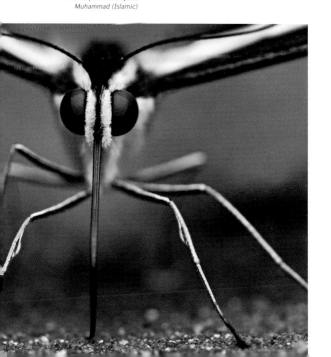

6   *Monday*

7   *Tuesday*   *Full moon*

8   *Wednesday*

Goliath
by Douglas David Seifert
'I found this goliath grouper, with its massive mouth and swirling mane of silver fish, lurking in a shipwreck off Jupiter, Florida. The cigar minnows are clustering around it to protect themselves from other predators such as trevally, a type of fish.' Groupers feed mainly on crustaceans such as lobsters. The goliath grouper is the largest reef fish in the Atlantic, up to 2.5 metres long and weighing up to 363 kilogrammes – large individuals such as this one are rare.

Canon EOS 1Ds Mark II + 15mm fisheye lens; 1/250 sec at f8.

13 *Monday*

14 *Tuesday*   *St Valentine's Day*

15 *Wednesday*

16 *Thursday*

17 *Friday*

18 *Saturday*

19 *Sunday*

Starling genie
by Barış Koca
'I was at Lake Mogan, near Ankara in Turkey.
The lake was frozen so I was able to stand
facing the reeds with the sun behind me, as
a thousand-strong flocks of starlings wheeled
in over the horizon to merge into dense
super-flocks. Then, as the sun set, the birds
pirouetted into the spotlight of its rays, and
the perfect picture was created.'

*Canon EOS 30D + Sigma 18–200mm f3.5–6.3 DC
OS lens at 18mm; 1/320 sec at f9; ISO 200.*

20 *Monday*   *George Washington's Birthday, Holiday (USA)*

21 *Tuesday*   *New moon* ●
                                                        Shrove Tuesday (Christian)

22 *Wednesday*   *Ash Wednesday (Christian)*

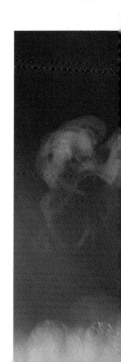

Black grouse dawn show
by Bence Máté
In the spring dawn, male black grouse all over
Europe put on a fabulous courtship display. 'I was
in Finland and for three hours, along with a handful
of nonchalant female grouse, watched four males
strut, march, fluff, flutter, flounce, shimmy, sashay,
"roo-roo-roo", leap and fight to be judged as the
fittest, most promising, most mateable male.
The females weren't so impressed: none of them
mated.' Black grouse are on the decline in western
Europe to the point of being extinct in many parts
of England. Conservation groups are trying to
save and re-introduce the species.

*Nikon D200 + Sigma 300–800mm f5.6 lens; 1/640
sec at f7.1; ISO 400; beanbag.*

23 *Thursday*

24 *Friday*

25 *Saturday*   **26** *Sunday*

27 *Monday*

28 *Tuesday*

29 *Wednesday*

1 *Thursday* *St David's Day (Wales)*

2 *Friday*

3 *Saturday*   **4** *Sunday*

Orcas at sunset
by Nuno Sá

Orcas, or killer whales, are top predators that hunt fish, birds and other marine mammals such as seals, other whales and dolphins. They hunt in pods made up of family members. 'As soon as I dropped into the water off São Miguel Island, in the Azores, one of the males spun round and came straight at me, its six-metre body stiff, as though about to attack. We looked each other in the eye. But I didn't feel any aggression from the whale, just curiosity. The day after, the pod killed a fin whale.'

Canon EOS 20D + Canon 70–200mm f4 IS USM lens at 70mm; 1/80 sec at f13; ISO 200.

5   *Monday*

6   *Tuesday*

7   *Wednesday*

8   *Thursday*   *Full moon* ○

9   *Friday*

10 *Saturday*

11 *Sunday*

Song of the corn bunting
by Gastone Pivatelli
In spring, the 'metallic' song of the corn bunting
rings out across the British countryside. The
males sing to attract as many females as possible
to their territories. 'I noticed the teasel plant was
this male's favourite song post, and so I set up
my camera early in the morning and waited for
it to arrive. The air was so cold, the steam of its
breath condensed into song-rings above.'

*Canon EOS 1Ds Mark II + Canon EF 500mm f4 IS
lens; 1/250 sec at f5.6; ISO 200; tripod.*

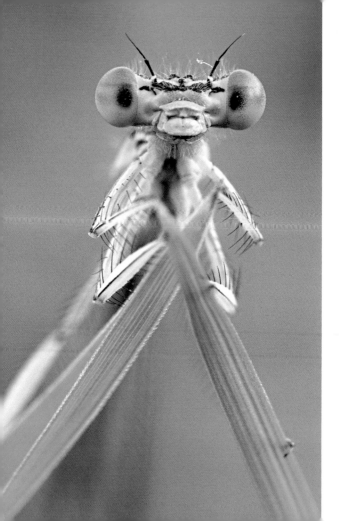

2 *Monday*

3 *Tuesday*

4 *Wednesday*

5 *Thursday*

6 *Friday*

7 *Saturday*   *St Patrick's Day (N. Ireland, Rep. Ireland)*

8 *Sunday*   *Mothering Sunday (UK)*

ye-to-eye
Theo Bosboom

his white-legged damselfly posed one May
vening on symmetrically crossed grasses.
fter a couple of photos from a distance, I
ept closer and closer, trying not to make any
nexpected movements. An hour or so later,
was really close. But it still maintained eye
ontact while I fired off shot after shot.' The
sulting detail reveals its beautiful colours and
s spiked hair and 'goatee' beard, together with
s armoury of sensory leg bristles.

*Canon EOS 30 with 100mm f2.8 macro lens,
25mm extension tube and 1.4x extender;
Fujichrome Velvia 50 rated at 40; tripod, cable
release and mirror lock-up.*

9 *Monday*   *St Patrick's Day, Holiday (N. Ireland, Rep. Ireland)*

0 *Tuesday*   *Spring Equinox*

1 *Wednesday*

2 *Thursday*   *New moon* ●

3 *Friday*

4 *Saturday*

5 *Sunday*   *British Summertime begins (BST)*

eat white torpedo

Amos Nachoum

arks are the most notorious predators in the
a and they survive by eating whales, seals
d dolphins and large fish. 'I spent two years
anning this project, in an area known as the
ng of Death, Seal Island, in South Africa, where
eat white sharks ambush seals. Sometimes
ey breach for seals, sometimes one would do
for a rubber dummy towed behind the boat,
here. It was always unexpected and over in
ss than a second.'

*Nikon F5 + 70–200mm f4 lens; 1/1000 sec;
Fujichrome Provia 100.*

....

26 *Monday*

....

27 *Tuesday*

....

28 *Wednesday*

....

29 *Thursday*

....

30 *Friday*

....

31 *Saturday*

....

1 *Sunday*

April Fool's D
Palm Sunday (Christia

Damsel emerging
by Ross Hoddinott
Just before its final moult, after two years in
the pond, instinct drove the larvae of a large
red damselfly up from the depths 'to climb a
reed, close to where I could position my tripod.
I allowed enough depth of field to keep the
damselfly and reed in sharp focus and the
background blurred,' says Ross. An hour later,
the insect took its first flight, leaving its
monster husk behind.

Nikon D70 with Sigma 150mm macro lens; 1/30
sec at f13; 200 ISO; Manfrotto tripod.

2   *Monday*

3   *Tuesday*

4   *Wednesday*

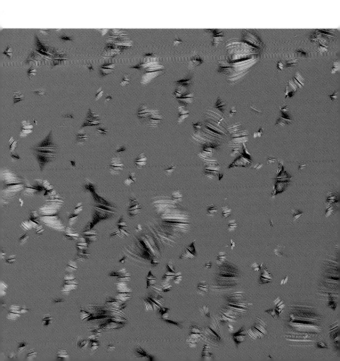

Flight of the butterflies
by Ingo Arndt
One of the world's most famous wildlife migrations
starts in Michoacán, Mexico. Every year in early
spring, about 400 million monarch butterflies
leave their overwintering site in the Sierra Madre
mountains to fly to North America – a journey of
more than 3,000 kilometres. Their bright colours
advertise the fact that they are foul-tasting and
poisonous to predators. 'I positioned myself in
a small clearing, where I could photograph the
clouds of monarchs passing overhead. I used
a long exposure to get a dynamic image of
movement. But there was just one day when
the sun shone into the clearing, and the sky
provided the brilliant blue backdrop I was after.'

*Canon EOS 5D + Canon 70–200mm f2.8 IS USM
lens; 1/45 sec at f32; ISO 100; tripod.*

Monday   Easter Monday (Christian) Holiday (UK excl Scotland, Rep. Ireland, Canada)

0 Tuesday

1 Wednesday

2 Thursday

3 Friday

4 Saturday   Last day of Passover (Jewish)

5 Sunday

Curious calf
by Jordi Chias
'Pilot whale mothers spend years attentively
caring for their calves and only breed every seven
or eight years. While sailing between the Canary
Islands and Madeira, Jordi slipped into the water.
The mother at first kept between me and the
infant, but after a while lost interest. The calf
came straight up to me and stayed motionless
just a metre away. I took a few shots, but then I
lowered my camera and simply looked the calf in
the eye – a moment I will never forget.'

*Nikon D70s + Nikon 12–24mm lens at 18mm;
1/80 sec at f5.6; ISO 200; Hugyfot housing;
no strobes.*

16 *Monday*

17 *Tuesday*

18 *Wednesday*

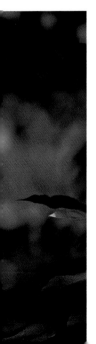

Golden leaf monkey
by Bernard Castelein
This wary individual, with its beautiful coat
spotlit by sunshine, fulfilled Bernard's ambition
to photograph a golden leaf monkey in the wild.
These highly endangered langurs, threatened by
logging, are confined to forest remnants in the
Himalayan foothills on the border of Assam, in
India and Bhutan. They live in the treetops and
so are extremely difficult to photograph. 'I finally
found a group that would allow me close enough
to use a long lens,' says Bernard, 'but even then
they were very nervous.'

*Nikon D2x with Nikkor AFS 500mm f4 lens; 1/500
sec at f4; 200 ISO.*

23 Monday

24 Tuesday

25 Wednesday

26 Thursday

27 Friday

28 Saturday

29 Sunday

Snappers in synchrony
by Alexander Mustard
Guraidhoo Corner is off the edge of the South
Malé coral atoll in the Maldives and attracts
many reef sharks. Paddletail snappers in this
exposed environment respond to anything
bigger than them, including a human diver, by
bunching into a tight, defensive ball. 'The shape
of the formation continually morphed as the
fish jostled for position,' says Alex.

*Nikon D2x with 17–35mm AFS lens; 1/100 sec at
f6.3; 100 ISO; Subal underwater housing.*

30 *Monday*

1 *Tuesday*

2 *Wednesday*

Monkey moment
by Patrick Corning
'I went on holiday with my parents to Costa
Rica. Monkeys used to pick fruit from the trees
around our villa,' says Patrick. 'They stayed for a
long time, so I had time to take some pictures
of them playing.' Squirrel monkeys are one of
the smaller New World species. They live in large
groups but split into smaller groups during the
day to feed on berries, fruits, seeds, insects and
small invertebrates. Like many New World
species, they are vulnerable to habitat loss.

*Nikon D50 + 75–300mm f4.5–5.6 lens; 1/40 sec
at f5.6; ISO 200; tripod.*

7 *Monday*   *Early May Holiday (UK, Rep. Ireland*

8 *Tuesday*

9 *Wednesday*

10 *Thursday*

11 *Friday*

12 *Saturday*

13 *Sunday*   *Mother's Day (USA, Canada, Australia*

Sparrowhawk on the lookout
by Fergus Gill

Sparrowhawks now live and hunt in urban areas
of the UK and not just in woodlands. 'After
school, I camped out in our back garden. I had
built a hide near a rowan tree, making sure I
had a clear view of one particular branch – the
favourite perch of a male sparrowhawk. This one
came to our garden several times a day to hunt
the newly fledged house sparrows.'

*Nikon D200 + Nikon 200–400mm f4 lens; 1/15
sec at f4; ISO 400; tripod; dome hide.*

14 *Monday*

15 *Tuesday*

16 *Wednesday*

17 *Thursday*

Ascension Day (Christian

18 *Friday*

Olympic Torch Rela

19 *Saturday*

20 *Sunday*

New moon

Ocean glider
by Marguerite Fewkes
Flying fish fly by beating their tail fins to build
up speed for take off. They then glide on the
huge pectoral fins either side of their body for
up to an astonishing 100 metres. 'One afternoon,
dozens of large flying fish appeared off the
bow of our boat sailing between Vanuatu in
the South Pacific and Fiji. Their blue sheen was
dazzling against the velvety sea.'

*Canon EOS 20D + Canon 75–300mm IS DO zoom
lens; 1/500 sec at f7.1; ISO 200.*

....

1 *Monday*

....

2 *Tuesday*

....

3 *Wednesday*

....

4 *Thursday*

....

5 *Friday*

....

6 *Saturday*

....

7 *Sunday*

Soft-coral community
by David Hall

Soft corals are one of my favourite subjects
and this particular colony in Indonesia was
unusually colourful. A shy goby was living with
the colony, and I decided to make it the focus
of the composition.' Many animals like goby fish
use soft-coral colonies for shelter. These animals
are either transparent or similar in colour to the
coral to help camouflage them.

*Canon EOS 5D + Canon 100mm macro lens;
1/200 sec at f20; ISO 200; Subal housing; two
Ikelite DS-51 strobes.*

28   *Monday*   *Memorial Day. Holiday (US*

29   *Tuesday*

30   *Wednesday*

1 *Thursday*

Friday

Saturday   **3** *Sunday*   Trinity Sunday (Christian)

Bee-eater ballet
by Chris van Rooyen

'A boat on the Zambezi in Namibia was the perfect hide to observe bee-eaters. They never stopped chirruping to each other as they chased insects and I had the impression some were just having fun. They would weave around in the wind, hover in the updraft created by the riverbank, then fold their wings to parachute back into the nest-hole.' With its vivid red plumage, the carmine bee-eater is one of Africa's most striking birds. They are a social species, breeding in colonies of many hundreds of birds.

Canon EOS-1D Mark II + Canon EF 500mm f4 IS USM lens + 1.4x II teleconverter; 1/2500 sec at f8; ISO 400; Manfrotto 055CL tripod + 501 friction head.

4   Monday

5   Tuesday

6   Wednesday

Deadlock
by David Maitland
'A cat-eyed tree-snake was locked in an embrace
with a Morelet's tree frog. The kicking frog
showed no sign of weakening. And the stubborn
snake wouldn't budge. It was a complete
stalemate. Three hours later, I realised the first
one to give in would, in fact, be me – and I went
to bed.' When the rains come to the forests of
Belize, the tree frogs descend after dark from the
canopy, gathering around the puddles and ponds.
Found only in a few areas of northern Central
America and Mexico, the Morelet's tree frog is
a critically endangered species due to habitat
destruction and disease.

Canon EOS-1Ds Mark II + 100mm macro lens;
1/500 sec at f10; ISO 50; twin flashes.

11 *Monday*

12 *Tuesday*

13 *Wednesday*

Meerkat moment
by Shem Compion
Meerkats are extremely vigilant – their lives depend
on them spotting raptors flying overhead. They
also live in colonies and are highly social, teaching
their young, for example, how to extract stings
from insects. 'This pup and its siblings were with an
adult babysitter, in South Africa's Tswalu Kalahari
Reserve. As they sat out in the sun, a hornet flew
by. Usually very vigilant animals, always on the
look out, thoughts of danger immediately turned
to those of lunch and for a moment, these two
were transfixed.'

*Nikon D200 + Nikon 200–400mm f4 VR lens; 1/320
sec at f8; ISO 100; beanbag.*

14 Thursday

15 Friday

16 Saturday

17 Sunday

*Father's Day
(UK, USA, Canada, Australia)*

18 *Monday*

19 *Tuesday* *New moon* ●

20 *Wednesday* *Summer Solstice*

21 *Thursday*

22 *Friday*

23 *Saturday*

24 *Sunday*

Sand sprinters
by Dan Mead
The southern ostrich lives in southern Africa
and is nomadic, foraging for seeds and insects
as it goes. 'The mother was in the lead, scouting
the situation ... But its next move took me by
surprise. It suddenly turned sharp right and
headed straight up the nearest dune. It must
have been 100 metres high and at an angle of
30 degrees. The sand slipped away under their
feet. It was an amazing effort. The whole family
disappeared over the crest of the Namibian dune.'

*Canon EOS 5D + Canon 100–400mm f4.5–5.6 IS
USM lens at 400mm; 1/640 sec at f9; ISO 100.*

25 *Monday*

26 *Tuesday*

27 *Wednesday*

Troublemaker
by Stefano Unterthiner
'I nicknamed this young adult Troublemaker.
He was interested in me, so getting a close-up
wasn't difficult. But he would leap at me and
kick off my back like a trampoline. It was part
play, part confrontation, part attention-seeking,
part curiosity. I think Troublemaker's expression
captures the spirit of these wonderful monkeys.'
Black-crested macaques live on the Indonesian
island of Sulawesi. They usually forage in the
forests, but sometimes their search for food takes
them out of the forest and onto the beach. They
wander along scouring the rocks for fallen fruits
and nuts or, in the case of the young ones, to
paddle in the waves.

Nikon D2x + Nikon 12–24mm lens; 1/250 sec at
f10; ISO 125; graduated neutral-density filter; flash.

8 *Thursday*

9 *Friday*

0 *Saturday*   **1** *Sunday*   Canada Day

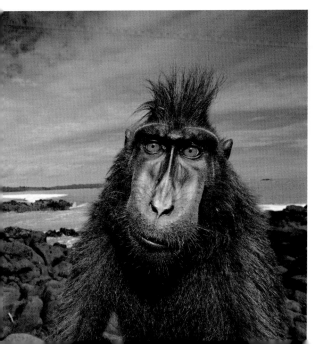

Monday
Canada Day, Holiday (Canada)

Tuesday
Full moon ○

Wednesday
Independence Day, Holiday (USA)

Thursday

Friday

Saturday

Sunday

awn meadow
y Rupert Heath

tend to take most of my photographs
round dawn – the most magical time to be
utside. This picture's main focus is the field
cabious, but you can also see the old grass
pecies, and there's a wonderful, thick, uncut
edgerow beyond.' The National Trust cares
or this meadow in Surrey, UK.

*Ebony 45S + 90mm lens; 13 sec at f32;
Fujichrome Velvia 50; 0.9 and 0.3 hard-graduated
neutral-density Lee filters; tripod.*

9 *Monday*

10 *Tuesday*

11 *Wednesday*

Eyes in the oasis
by Lee Slabber
Lee was photographing some oryx bones in
Kgalagadi Transfrontier Park, South Africa, when
he felt himself being watched. 'I turned to face
a beautiful young male leopard. A moment later
it fled, as shocked to see me as I was to see it.'
Leopards are usually solitary hunters, using a
combination of opportunism, camouflage, stealth
and speed. They will stalk their prey and can be
as little as two metres away before they make a
short, fast rush and then pounce.

Canon EOS-1D Mark III + Canon EF 600mm lens;
1/250 sec at f5.7; ISO 200.

2 *Thursday*   *Battle of the Boyne, Holiday (N. Ireland)*

3 *Friday*

4 *Saturday*   **15** *Sunday*   *St Swithin's Day (Christian)*

6   *Monday*

7   *Tuesday*

8   *Wednesday*

9   *Thursday*   *New moon* ●

0   *Friday*   *Ramadan begins (Islamic)*

1   *Saturday*

2   *Sunday*

etal procession
Adrian Hepworth

discovered this scattering of tonka-bean-tree
etals on the forest floor in Costa Rica and,
re enough, there was a column of industrious
orker ants busily transporting the petals away.
chose a slow shutter to create the pink blur
d a flash at the end of the two seconds so
e ants would stand out.'

*Canon EOS 5D + Canon 20mm f2.8 lens; 2 sec at
f22; ISO 200; second curtain flash; tripod.*

23   Monday

24   Tuesday

25   Wednesday

26   Thursday

27   Friday   *Olympic Games opening ceremo*

28   Saturday

29   Sunday

Pool hawk
by Bence Máté
'If a bird sees you move, it gets spooked, so
you can't adjust or change your lens. So I use a
one-way "mirror" fixed to the front of my hide.
This sparrowhawk spent an hour preening and
occasionally leaning forward to sip, relaxed and
unaware I was there.' Sparrowhawks are fierce-
looking hunters. They eat other birds, usually
smaller species such as finches and thrushes, but
also those as large as woodpigeons. Sparrowhawks   *Nikon D200 + Nikon MF 300mm f2.8 lens; 1/10*
are very agile fliers and do not hover like kestrels.   *sec at f2.8; tripod; hide.*

0 *Monday*

31 *Tuesday*

1 *Wednesday*

2 *Thursday*   *Full moon* ○

3 *Friday*

4 *Saturday*

5 *Sunday*

'ye of the minke
y Jürgen Freund

warf minke whales travel to the northern
art of Australia's Great Barrier Reef between
une and August, possibly to breed. 'I spent a
week on the *Undersea Explorer*, a research and
live boat. In snorkelling gear, we hung from a
ne behind the boat and drifted, so as not to
righten the whales. This six- to seven-metre
warf minke whale turned up, treating us to
are displays of underwater pirouetting. I felt
he was looking straight at me.'

*Nikon D200 + Nikkor 12–24mm f4 lens; 1/180
auto; Seacam housing.*

6   *Monday*   *Summer Holiday (Scotland, Rep. Ireland*

7   *Tuesday*

8   *Wednesday*

Underworld
by Brian Skerry

'A blue cod was taking a stroll on its fins through an otherworldly garden of vibrantly coloured sea pens and starfish. Through careful use of flash, I brought them to light. Fragile marine areas such as this one still exist in New Zealand waters thanks to federal protection.' Sea pens prefer deep water and are rarely found in waters less than ten metres deep. But in the shallow waters of Long Sound Marine Reserve tannin-stained surface water blocks out sunlight, tricking sea pens into settling at shallower depths. Sea pen colonies orientate themselves in the path of the currents, to ensure a steady flow of food particles.

Nikon D2x + 16mm lens; 1/30 sec at f9; ISO 200; Subal housing; two Hartenberger strobes on 1/4 power, additional strobe used to light more distant subjects.

3 *Monday*

4 *Tuesday*

5 *Wednesday*

6 *Thursday*

7 *Friday*   New moon ●

18 *Saturday*

19 *Sunday*   *Ramadan ends (Islamic)*

Golden-crowned sifaka
by Pete Oxford
Golden-crowned sifakas are among the world's
most endangered primates and they are confined
to dry forest in the Daraina area of northern
Madagascar. 'I watched them for a while,' says
Pete, 'charmed by their deft leaps through the
trees and their stunning looks.' This individual
came to a sudden halt and peered from behind
the tree trunk. 'A wonderful moment of contact.'

*Nikon D2x with 300mm f2.8 lens and 1.4x
teleconverter; 1/125 sec at f5.6; tripod; flash.*

20 *Monday*

21 *Tuesday*

22 *Wednesday*

Beast of the sediment
by Göran Ehlmé

The walrus is a bottom-feeder. To get to the bivalve shells it first roots, pig-like, with its snout or beats a flipper, to whip up the sediment. Then it uses its facial bristles to brush away the sediment so that it can get to the bivalves. Swimming with this huge beast off northeast Greenland, Göran took more than 400 images, shooting from every angle. Hours later, 'the moment came', says Göran. 'The walrus looked round, and we made eye contact.'

Nikon D2x with 12–24mm lens; 1/50 sec at f4; 400 ISO; Seacam housing with wide-angle port.

27 *Monday*

28 *Tuesday*

29 *Wednesday*

Dewdrops
by Juhani Kosonen
'When I look at this picture, I think of the universe
– of planets and stars.' Juhani has photographed
dew many times on the same windowpane and
is always astonished at how it can change. 'A tiny
shift in the light affects the reflected array of
colours and can make a dramatic difference.' In
this case, the picture was created at night, with
the only light reflected in the droplets coming
from outside. A slight change in camera angle or
focus point generated a totally different scene
but this was the composition he finally chose.

*Canon EOS 10D with Sigma 105mm f2.8 macro
lens; 13 sec at f2.8; 100 ISO; tripod.*

September 2012

3 Monday

4 Tuesday

5 Wednesday

6 Thursday

7 Friday

8 Saturday

9 Sunday

Paralympic Games en

Boletus in the rain
by Thierry Van Baelinghem
'The Monts du Lyonnais woods near my
home outside Lyon are full of mushrooms and
toadstools. Lying on the soggy leaf-litter, the
challenge was to keep my equipment dry. I
waited until the sun was soft enough to bring
out the delicate colour of the bolete and
surrounding moss, and then I used the rain
to enhance the toadstool's organic form.'

*Nikon D100 + 60mm f2.8G ED AF-S micro Nikko
lens; 1/60 sec at f5.6; ISO 200.*

10 *Monday*

11 *Tuesday*

12 *Wednesday*

Swamp cypress
by Cece Fabbro
'The scene in Lake Martin, Louisiana, seemed so serene, so quiet. Yet it was anything but. All day the birds squawk, squeak and bark over mates, nesting sites and nest-building materials. This isolated cluster of ancient swamp cypress fascinated me. In the early morning mist there was something mystical, almost eerie about them.' Swamp cypress has a great tolerance to flooding – it grows wooden root extensions that poke out of the water line to help the roots get oxygen. Lake Martin is home to more than 20,000 breeding herons, egrets, white ibises, roseate spoonbills, owls and ospreys.

Canon EOS-1Ds Mark II + 28–135mm f3.5–5.6 lens at 50mm; 1/100 sec at f22; Gitzo tripod + Kirk ballhead.

3 *Thursday*

4 *Friday*

5 *Saturday*   **16** *Sunday*   *New moon* ●

17 *Monday*   *Rosh Hashanah (Jewish New Yea*

18 *Tuesday*

19 *Wednesday*

Leaf drop
by Darran Leal

In 2006, the rainforest in far north Queensland in Australia was rich in nature and opportunities to take wildlife photographs. Then Cyclone Larry reduced the area to stumps and tangled undergrowth. This photograph was taken a year later. 'Picking my way through the ruins I came across a small tree backlit by the sun and sparkling with rain. A jewel-like drop, with its perfect reflection of leaves inside, struck me as a great symbol of the regrowth of the rainforest, but I had to move fast. The challenge was to capture the moment in spite of gusts of wind and the great magnification required.'

Canon EOS 5D + 100mm macro lens; 1/125 sec at f22; ISO 100; Canon 580EX flash + TTL auto cord.

24 *Monday*

25 *Tuesday*

26 *Wednesday*

Yom Kippur (Jewis

27 *Thursday*

28 *Friday*

29 *Saturday*

30 *Sunday*

Full moon

London tern
by Jack Chapman
'By the River Lee Navigation canal, near my
home in London, UK, I found common terns
flying in to drink and feed. I caught this one
as it passed the reflection of a scarlet canal
boat, its wings skimming the surface.' The
common tern is a silvery-grey and white bird,
distinguished from the similar Arctic tern by
the black tip of its red bill.

*Canon EOS 350D + 400mm f5.6 lens; 1/400 sec
at f5.6; ISO 100.*

1 *Monday*

2 *Tuesday*

3 *Wednesday*

Flight of the mouse-eared bat
by Carsten Braun
'After helping scientists catch and ring greater
mouse-eared bats in a cave in Mayen, Germany,
I photographed their release. The challenge was
to set up the cameras, flashes and cables in the
right place, in the pitch darkness with only a head-
torch.' The greater mouse-eared bat spends four
to five hours a day hunting insects in the air and
on the ground, before returning to roost. Greater
mouse-eared bats often use attics to rear their
young though they prefer caves for hibernation
in wintertime.

*Canon EOS 5D + 70–200mm f2.8 lens; 1/200 sec
at f16; ISO 100; four Canon 550EX flashes + light-
beam sensor.*

October 2012

8 *Monday*

9 *Tuesday*

10 *Wednesday*

Daddy long legs
by Jordi Chias

'I came across this strange arrangement of spikes and spines while diving near Puerto de Mogán off the southern coast of Gran Canaria in the Canary Islands. I thought the spikes and tangle of long legs made a wonderfully graphic image, and the cobalt blue background with a school of small silver fish flitting past was like a sky of stars.' This large male arrow crab is standing guard over his mate, who has a swollen abdomen full of bright orange eggs, preventing other males from mating with her.

Canon EOS 5D + 17–40mm f4 lens at 40mm; 1/40 sec at f11; ISO 100; Sea & Sea housing; two Sea & Sea YS110 strobes.

15 *Monday*

New moon ●

16 *Tuesday*

17 *Wednesday*

Moon fire on Cerro Chaltén
by Jordi Busqué Pérez
'The top of Cerro Chaltén, which means smoking
mountain, is nearly always covered by cloud. But
a few times a year, when the moon is in the right
position, you can see it "on fire". Camping at the
foot of the Argentinean side of the mountain,
I used a long exposure to capture the swirls of
cloud and the star trails.'

*Nikon D70s + AF-S DX VR Nikkor 18–200mm f3.5–
5.6G IF-ED lens; 6 min at 44mm f4.5; ISO 200;
cable, mini-tripod.*

22   *Monday*

23   *Tuesday*

24   *Wednesday*

Frog refuge
by Ines Labunski Roberts
'One winter morning I found this huddle of young
American bullfrogs in an open drainpipe. They were
near a thermal pool in the foothills of California's
Sierra Nevada, and some were swimming in it. Dead
frogs nearby could have been victims of a severe
frost the previous night. The drain and the warmth
from the pool might have saved these six.' The
American bullfrog is native to North America, and
usually green or brown. Adults can grow up to
20 centimetres in length but the frogs pictured
were just a little bigger than 2.54 centimetres.

*Canon EOS 20D + Canon 24–85mm lens; 1/200
sec probably at f8.*

October – November 2012

29 *Monday*

30 *Tuesday*

31 *Wednesday*

Land of the quiver trees
by Werner Van Steen
'When I arrived at the Quiver Tree Forest in Namibia I wanted to take the first plane home. I'd heard so much about these surreal plants but they looked dull and grey. But when I went back at sunset, the colours had intensified and I was overwhelmed by their beauty.' The soft pulpy inner tissue of its branches is easily hollowed out by bushmen to make quivers for their arrows, hence the name.

Fuji GX 617 + 90mm f5.6 lens; Fujichrome Velvia 50.

Thursday   *All Saints' Day (Christian)*

Friday

Saturday   **4**   Sunday

---

5 *Monday*   *Guy Fawkes Night (U...*

---

6 *Tuesday*

---

7 *Wednesday*

Colourful business
by Noam Kortler

'Fish that cruise past get a quick clean – whether
they want one or not. Most big reef fish, though,
make a point of turning up at the cleaning station
for a daily grooming session, which can last several
minutes. Queues can form as reef fish wait their
turn.' Moses Rock, off the coast of Eilat, Israel, is
a regular cleaning station for large reef fish. Big
fish, like the dazzling bullethead parrotfish, hold
their mouth open so a little cleaner fish can peck
inside for parasites. The cleaner fish advertises
its identity, and its services, with its black-striped
costume and a special jerky swim.

*Nikon D2x + Nikon 105mm f2.8G VR micro lens;
1/125 sec at f13; ISO 100; Seacam housing; two
Ikelite DS125 strobes.*

Thursday

Friday

Saturday   **11** Sunday   *Armistice Day/*
                                 Remembrance Sunday
                                 Veterans Day (USA)

··

12   *Monday*   *Veterans Day, Holiday (US*

··

13   *Tuesday*   *New moon*
                                              Diwali (Hindu, Si

··

14   *Wednesday*

··

15   *Thursday*   *Al-Hijira/Islamic New Year (Islam*

··

16   *Friday*

··

17   *Saturday*

··

18   *Sunday*

Polar sunrise
by Miguel Lasa
In autumn polar bears gather around Churchill
on Canada's Hudson Bay waiting for the sea to
freeze over, eager to feed on seals. 'So many of
the photographs I'd seen of polar bears failed
to show the power of the animals or any sense
of the harshness of the polar environment.
While the bears paced the beach waiting for
the ice, I waited for the perfect light. Finally I
got the shot I was after – a bear backlit by the
first rays of sunlight.'

*Canon EOS 40D + Canon EF500mm f4 IS USM
lens; 1/1250 sec at f4 (+2/3 compensation);
ISO 400.*

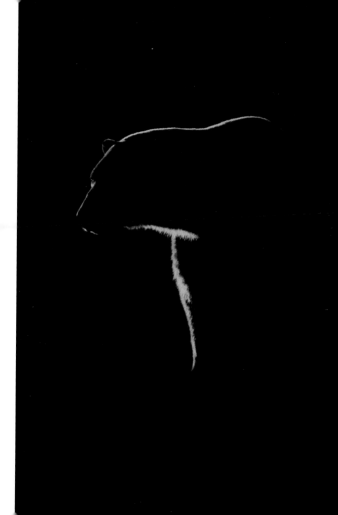

19 *Monday*

20 *Tuesday*

21 *Wednesday*

Great barracuda
by Tibor Dombovári
The barracuda has a protruding lower jaw, formidable teeth and thuggish expression. Tibor, however, saw only beauty when he came across this great barracuda lurking beneath his dive boat in Papua New Guinea. 'I grabbed a tank of air and a wide-angle lens,' he says, 'and jumped straight in. We were mutually curious and followed each other around for nearly two hours.' Great barracudas are top-of-the-range, opportunistic predators, with huge, powerful jaws that enable them to eat a variety of prey.

Nikon D70s with Nikkor 12–24mm f4G AFS DX lens; 1/200 sec at f7.1; 200 ISO; Subal housing, two Ikelite DS125 strobes.

26 *Monday*

27 *Tuesday*

28 *Wednesday*   *Full moon*

29 *Thursday*

30 *Friday*   *St Andrew's Day, Holiday (Scotlan*

1 *Saturday*

2 *Sunday*

Emperor elegance
by Jan Vermeer
'I have visited emperor penguins many times,
so I knew what to do: sit in one place and
watch. I wanted to use a long lens, to get close
without disturbing them. In particular I wanted
to capture the elegant moment the adults greet
each other.' Emperor penguins are the largest
of the 17 penguin species and they live on the
Antarctic ice. In November, Snow Hill Island
is home to about 4,000 breeding pairs, each   *Nikon D2x + 500mm f4 lens; 1/350 sec at f8;*
incubating a single chick.   *Gitzo tripod.*

3   *Monday*

4   *Tuesday*

5   *Wednesday*

Big fish, little fishes
by Gavin Parsons
The world's largest fish, whale sharks, can be up
to 20 metres long and gather off Mafia Island,
Tanzania, between November and January. They
come to filter-feed on the masses of plankton
there. Local fishermen use them to locate shoals
of small fish, which shelter around them, and
Gavin used fishing boats to locate the giants.
'We found a shark being shadowed by a couple
of boats. It moved under our boat and just hung
there, possibly sheltering from the glare. As I
slipped into the sea and it lifted its huge head,
the little fishes fled for fear of being chased to
the surface.'

*Nikon D70 with 16mm fisheye lens; 1/125 sec
at f8; 200 ISO; Sea & Sea housing with fisheye
dome port.*

Thursday

Friday

Saturday

9 Sunday
Chanukah,
Festival of Lights begins (Jewish)

10 *Monday*

11 *Tuesday*

12 *Wednesday*

4 *Friday*

5 *Saturday*   **16** *Sunday*   *Chanukah,*
                                              Festival of Lights ends (Jewish)

Last breath of autumn
by Michal Budzynski

Michal was photographing the famous autumnal
colours of the firs, beeches, larch and spruce trees
on the Pieniny Mountains in southern Poland.
'The previous day had been sunny, but overnight
snow extinguished the glow. As we drove down
the mountain, I looked back and glimpsed in the
distance a single last glowing patch of gold. For
some reason, the snow must have slid off the
branches of the beech trees but stuck to the firs,
creating the breathtaking view.'

*Nikon D80 + Nikkor 300mm lens; 1/400 sec at f5.6;
ISO 125.*

December 2012

17 *Monday*

18 *Tuesday*

19 *Wednesday*

Snow swans
by Yongkang Zhu
The Rongcheng Swan Lake nature reserve in eastern China is a major overwintering sanctuary for whooper swans. When the fresh water freezes, the birds are forced to feed in the fields, digging through the snow for grass. 'To photograph the swans in their environment meant I had to endure the same conditions – snowstorms and high winds that roll the snow across the flat land in great waves. The storm was so bitter I wished I could have escaped along with the swans.'

Canon EOS 20D + Sigma 300–800mm f5.6 lens at 300mm; 1/1250 sec at f6.3; ISO 200; tripod.

0 *Thursday*

1 *Friday* *Winter Solstice*

2 *Saturday*

23 *Sunday*

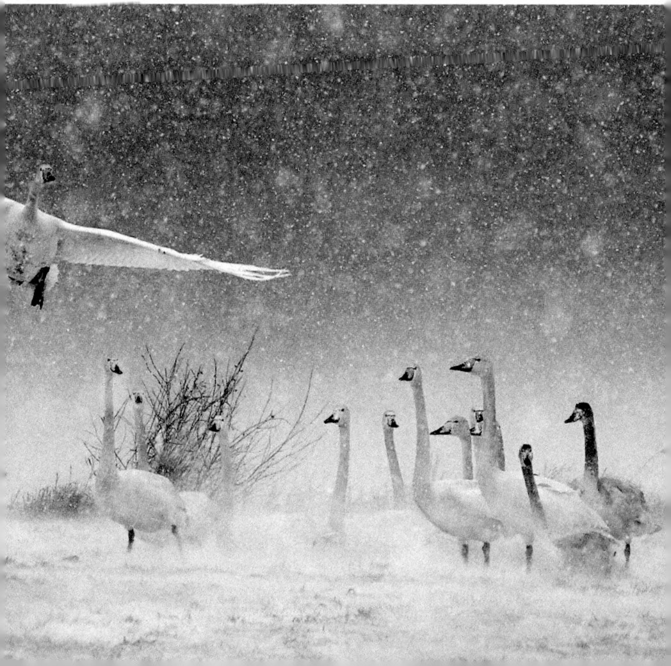

24 *Monday*

25 *Tuesday*

26 *Wednesday*

27 *Thursday*

28 *Friday*

29 *Saturday*   **30** *Sunday*

31 *Monday*

Stoat sandwich
by Ari Tervo
'When I heard a stoat was scavenging scraps
under a friend's bird table in the city of Kajaani,
Finland, I set up watch, armed with bread. The
stoat soon got the hang of retrieving slices, but
she moved so fast it took several hours and 20
slices for me to get the shot.' Stoats are excellent
foragers and in summer they are a chocolate
brown, but are camouflaged in winter when their
coats turn white.

*Canon EOS 1D Mark II + Canon 100–400 EF
f4.5–5.6 L IS lens; 1/500 sec; ISO 400 (+1/3
exposure compensation).*

Index of photographers

WEEK 32
urgen Freund *(Germany/Australia)*
eundfactory@gmail.com
ww.jurgenfreund.com
rent
ww.naturepl.com

WEEK 28
Rupert Heath *(UK)*
rdmheath@yahoo.co.uk

WEEK 46
Noam Kortler *(Israel)*
nemodive@netvision.net.il
www.nemodivers.co.il

WEEK 24
David Maitland *(UK)*
dpmaitland@googlemail.
com
www.davidmaitland.com

WEEK 30
Adrian Hepworth *(UK)*
adrian@hepworthimages.
com
www.hepworthimages.
com

WEEK 36
Juhani Kosonen
(Finland)
juhani.kosonen@kymp.net

EEK 20
rgus Gill *(UK)*
rgus.gill@houmail.co.uk
ww.scottishnature
photography.com
rent
ww.naturepl.com

WEEK 44
Ines Labunski Roberts
(UK/USA)
inesr@cox.net

WEEKS 9 & 31
Bence Máté *(Hungary)*
bence@bencemate.hu
www.matebence.hu
Agent
ferenc@hidephotography.
com

WEEK 14
Ross Hoddinott *(UK)*
info@rosshoddinott.
co.uk
www.rosshoddinott.
co.uk
Agent
www.naturepl.com

COVER & WEEK 47
Miguel Lasa *(UK/Spain)*
miguel.lasa@btinternet.
com
www.miguellasa.com

WEEK 26
Dan Mead *(USA)*
dansal@mac.com
www.meadeaglephotos.
com

EEK 22
vid Hall *(USA)*
vid@seaphotos.com
ww.seaphotos.com

WEEK 39
Darran Leal *(Australia)*
darran@worldadventures.
com.au
www.worldadventures.
com.au

WEEK 1
Vincent Munier *(France)*
contact@vincentmunier.
com
www.vincentmunier.com
Agent
www.naturepl.com

EEK 6
l Harbin *(USA)*
harb@comcast.net

WEEK 8
Barış Koca *(Turkey)*
bariskoca@hotmail.com
www.bariskoca.com

WEEK 18
Alexander Mustard
(UK)
alex@amustard.com
www.amustard.com

WEEK 13
Amos Nachoum
(Israel/USA)
amos@biganimals.com
www.biganimals.com

WEEK 2
Baard Næss *(Norway)*
baar-na@online.no

WEEK 34
Pete Oxford *(UK)*
pete@peteoxford.com
www.peteoxford.com
Agent
www.mindenpictures.com

WEEK 50
Gavin Parsons *(UK)*
gavin@h2o-images.co.uk
www.h2o-images.co.uk

WEEK 11
Gastone Pivatelli *(Italy)*
crex@libero.it

WEEK 10
Nuno Sá *(Portugal)*
fotonunosa@gmail.com
www.photonunosa.com

WEEK 7
Douglas David Seifert
(USA)
douglasseifert@mac.com
www.douglasseifert.com

WEEK 33
Brian Skerry *(USA)*
brian@brianskerry.com
www.brianskerry.com
Agent
www.ngsimages.com

WEEK 29
Lee Slabber
(South Africa)
slabber@rocketmail.com
www.leeslabber.com

WEEKS 53 & 54
Ari Tervo *(Finland)*
ari.tervo@kajaani.net

WEEK 27
Stefano Unterthiner
(Italy)
info@stefanounterthiner.
com
www.stefanounterthiner.
com

WEEK 37
**Thierry Van
Baelinghem** *(France)*
naturenimage@gmail.com

WEEK 23
Chris van Rooyen
(South Africa)
chris@wildlifephotograph.
co.za
www.wildlifephotograph.
co.za

WEEK 45
Werner Van Steen
(Belgium)
info@wernervansteen.
com
www.wernervansteen.co

WEEK 49
Jan Vermeer
(The Netherlands)
janvermeer.foto@plane
www.janvermeer.nl
Agent
www.fotonatura.com

WEEK 52
Yongkang Zhu *(China)*
zhu_yong_kang@126.
com

First published by the Natural History Museum, Cromwell Road, London SW7 5BD
© Natural History Museum, London, 2012
Photographs © the individual photographers
Text based on original captions used in the Wildlife Photographer of the Year
exhibitions
ISBN: 978 0 565 09288 7